"This re is a very practical how-to document, full of specific suggestions for those to whom life hands the difficult assignment of living with and supplying tender loving care to a patient."

— *Steve Allen*

"An extraordinary mixture of love and courage, *Care for the Caretaker* raises all the issues and tells you how to deal with them."

— *Sherwood Schwartz*, creator of "The Brady Bunch" and "Gilligan's Island"

"A magnificent testament to loving, caring, endurance, and the blessings of a triumphant marriage/partnership — to say nothing of the blessings it could provide for the reader facing a similar problem."

— *Hume Cronyn*

"When we were on location shooting the pilot of *Gilligan's Island*, Jim was on the phone to Henny every day. He was never so happy as when she was around — if only on the phone."

— *Rod Amateau*, director, producer and writer

"A warm-hearted, compassionate story of love under tragic circumstances, told with humanity and humor. I wish I had had this book during my own husband's illness."

— *Sandra Gould Morse*, author and actress

"Jim [Backus] belongs to a very exclusive club. Its members include people like Fred Allen, Jonathan Winters, Richard Pryor, and Robin Williams."

> — *Perry Lafferty*, *producer, director and network programming chief*

"Warm and touching."

> — *Sidney Sheldon*

CARE FOR THE CARETAKER

How Jim Backus' Wife Did It
An Upbeat Guide
for Those Who Care for Others

by

Henny Backus

Jasper Publications, Inc.
Calabasas, California

Printed in the United States of America

Library of Congress Cataloging-in-Publication Data
Backus, Henny.
   Care for the Caretaker, How Jim Backus'
Wife Did It, and Upbeat Guide for Those Who Care
for Others

Library of Congress Catalog Card Number: 99-65845

ISBN 0-9663465-2-1

Jasper Publications, Inc.
22287 Mulholland Hwy, PMB 337
Calabasas, California 91302

OTHER BOOKS BY
HENNY AND JIM BACKUS

Rocks on the Roof
(in paperback: Only When I Laugh)

What Are You Doing After the Orgy?

Backus Strikes Back

Forgive Us Our Digressions

DEDICATION

To Dr. Kathy J. Segal
who gave me the idea for this book, and

to publisher Caroline Pfouts who "discovered" me.

ACKNOWLEDGMENTS

I should like to thank the wonderful healers who helped us in so many ways.

First of all to our beloved doctor, Douglas Forde, who would answer any questions, calm my fears, and help in any way he could at any hour of the day or night.

To Dr. Alan Enelow, Jim's psychoanalyst, who somehow managed to keep him in one piece.

To Becki Kerns, our great physical therapist. We took Jim to her in a wheelchair on his first visit, and he walked out. Becki kept his spirits up throughout the entire eleven years.

And to Tommy McKiernan, our pharmacist, who astonished us with his home telephone number, and always immediately delivered whatever we needed.

I send you all my love.

TABLE OF CONTENTS

"Jimmy"
A Foreword to *Care for the Caretaker*

by Perry Lafferty

When I was a kid barely a year out of college, CBS Radio, back in New York, assigned me to produce a one shot summer show that would feature new talent. It was called *Class of '41*. After auditioning literally hundreds of heavy-breathing young hopefuls (many of them older than I was) and making my final selections, I found myself faced with the fact that I had no script for the program and didn't have the least idea of how to go about writing one.

I asked the CBS press department to run a story that I was looking for writers. In the next issue of *Weekly Variety* my appeal was published. Of course, it turned out to be a terrible mistake to reveal this problem in the public press, because it resulted in desk drawers all over the five boroughs being opened and dumped on my desk at 485 Madison Avenue.

Out of this mountainous mass of material, one piece burrowed its way to the top of the pile where it sat silently, waiting to knock me for a loop. It was written by Jim Backus and his then collaborator, Larry Berns. It was hilarious and dealt with the ways to rebuff aggressive New York cab drivers who demanded that people utilize their services whether or not the victims wanted them. (In the event you aren't old enough to remember, there were more cabs than riders in Manhattan in the early '40s.)

After reading it, I immediately called Mr. Backus into my little office and questioned him as to his writing credits.

"I have none, dear boy," he announced in his resonant baritone. "I am an AC-tor."

Upon pressing him further, he revealed that he was temporarily at liberty and had written the script only out of a need to visit Horn & Hardart's (the cheapest decent meal in New York) at more or less regular intervals, and to pay the rent. When I inquired after his partner, Larry Berns, he explained that the man was unable to attend our meetings as he was busy practicing his chosen profession: selling hot jewelry on 48th Street. I signed the duo on the spot for — I believe it was — $25 apiece.

And that's how my friendship with Jim began. While we were working on the script, the funny lines and ideas tumbled out of his mouth at such a quick pace that the typewriter I was using started to smoke. His gift at seeing the humor beneath the surface of even the most serious subjects was extraordinary. Before we had finished the show, I knew that I was working with a very special person and a once-in-a-lifetime talent.

After the war, Jim and Henny deserted the Big Apple and went west to live. It wasn't long after that before Alan Young had hired him to play the richest man in the world, Hubert Updike, who said wonderful things like:

"By George, and I've got the money to buy George."

And:

"Last night I went for a ride in my car and listened to Guy Lombardo and his Royal Canadians."

"But you don't have a radio in your car, Mr. Updike."

"I know. I had Guy Lombardo and his Royal Canadians."

Of course, Alan Young had writers, and some good ones. But a lot of what came out of Hubert's mouth was born in Jimmy's brain.

Did you know that when a *Mr. Magoo* episode was to be made he would first be called into the studio and paraded before a long series of storyboards outlining the particular cartoon and that he would, extemporaneously, spout the lines that fit the situation — lines the animators would later draw for the near-sighted man to speak? Jimmy was the style, the essence of that legendary succession of happy moments for millions of movie-goers.

I can't comment on Jimmy's film career in the '50s because I wasn't out here in Hollywood then. But I know it was a long and good one, filled with first-rate comedy performances and several memorable dramatic ones. His ability to observe the human condition and comment on it expanded. As life for every one became more complicated, he kept pace with his humor. He smoothed the sharp edges and let the air out of any pompous balloons that floated around him.

In the early '60s, when my wife, Fran, and I finally had to accept the fact that television in New York City was becoming extinct, we moved to Los

Angeles. Jimmy told me I shouldn't be upset if a six foot, 15-year-old boy dressed only in the equivalent of a purple Spandex jock strap, came to take my proper, Dalton-bred daughter for a ride on the back of his Harley-Davidson.

"It's their way out here, Pierre," he said. "Besides, a motorcycle traveling at high speeds requires the driver to use both hands." I wasn't reassured.

Later, in the mid-60s, when I was a vice president at CBS, a series called *Gilligan's Island* was launched. Jim etched another memorable portrait in his gallery: Thurston Howell. I remember how many different time periods CBS assigned to the show. Whenever the powers-that-*were* perceived there was a weak spot in the schedule, good old *Gilligan's* would be dropped into the breach. After the fourth time the show had been shifted, Jim took careful aim and said:

"Network executives are like new brides. When they don't have anything else to do, they move the furniture around."

Jim belongs to a very exclusive club. Its members include people like Fred Allen, Jonathan Winters, Richard Pryor, and Robin Williams. Jim's ability to dissect, then comment upon the human condition was unsurpassed. His turn of phrase, the rhythms of his speaking style, the twists and turns he took on his way to an insight, were unique; his and his alone. I'm glad I have a CD in my head that I can turn on at will, and relish the great moments I had when Jim was "on" and cooking.

Of course, he was much more than a fine

artist.   He was the kindest man I have ever encountered. In all the years we were friends, we never had a cross word. He was generous with his time and talents and, always, he was loving.

I've known Henny almost as long as I knew Jim. Through their lifetime together, their bonding was total. It stood — it *stands* — as a deep and enduring monument to the love and respect of one person for another. It is something to be cherished by all of us fortunate enough to have basked in its warmth and light.

Many years ago, when it came time for a famous actor to leave this life, he said, "Dying is easy. Comedy is hard."

The observation didn't apply to Jim. For him, it was the reverse. Comedy was easy and dying was hard. It was only at the very end that he agreed to leave us. Right until then, he wanted to stay. He wanted just one more moment so he could say something that would make us smile — something that, however briefly, would lift the load from our shoulders.

Bon voyage, Jim. And may the wind always be at your back.

###

Perry Lafferty was Vice President Programs, Hollywood for the CBS Television Network and Senior Vice President Movies, Mini-Series and Special Projects for NBC Entertainment. In 1964 he won an Emmy for producing *The Danny Kaye Show*. In 1986 he won many awards, including the Peabody for producing *An Early Frost*, the first movie about AIDS. He is also the author of several published novels, including *The Downing of Flight Six Heavy* and *Jablonski of LA*. His published non-fiction works include *Birdies Sing and Everything*.

Chapter One

NOVEMBER 1978

NOVEMBER 1978

It was November 1978. Jim had just been evaluated and the doctors' suspicions were confirmed. It was Parkinson's disease.

Parkinson's disease? What was that? It was nowhere in my consciousness. Jim had always done every benefit he was asked to do, but there was never one for Parkinson's disease. There was no telethon for it, and no pleas for donations ever came in the mail. So what was this all about?

"Parkinson's cannot be diagnosed," they told me. "Only evaluated."

What did that mean? I was filled with a sense of unreality. I couldn't believe this was happening. How often have you heard those words? I was terrified. What was I supposed to do now? How could I help? Then I became filled with dread. I was paralyzed with fear. Scared stiff. Frightened to death. These are not clichés. This was panic.

As I began to read, and hear, and live with it, I started to understand. But the doctors could only give me so much help and advice. There was no place where I could go to learn how to cope with what was, progressively, being demanded of me. What I needed was someone who had been there and done it. Someone to lead the way. Someone to show me how to handle it. To shed a little light. These were really uncharted waters. To whom could I turn? I felt about five years old. What I really needed was a mommy, a big sister — someone! But there was no one out there.

Slowly I found that I could manage.

Somehow, I was beginning to swing it. I was lucky to have such great doctors, great friends, the best help in every way. How would it be if I had less? I learned through my doctors that there is readily available assistance for anyone who needs it, for almost all of the problems that will appear. But I would still have to discover how to cope by myself. And so will you.

Jimmy has been gone since July 3rd, 1989, and I am just now at the point where I have the perspective and the presence of mind to look back in a way that will be constructive, and maybe helpful. I will tell you everything as I remember it. Maybe these are some of the problems that you are experiencing or are still to encounter. My biggest challenge, and the chief contribution that I could make that his physicians could not, was how to keep Jim's spirits up — and mine! How was I to retain my health and preserve my strength through all this confusion and pressure?

I got all the textbooks and talked to doctors. From what I could gather, I would have to find a whole new way of living my life. So, little by little, throughout the almost eleven years of caring for my husband, I found it. I found my own way in my own way. Although you are no doubt doing the same thing, I hope that my journey will make yours a little bit easier. You will stumble and fall, as I did, but I will try to be your candle and shed a little light for you, if at times only a tiny, flickering one.

Remember one thing: nothing I say can take the place of professional guidance. Everything of a medical nature must be discussed with your doctors.

What I hope to do is to make your day-to-day living easier for you. I can now offer you what I often wished I had — someone who had walked this path and had somehow made it through.

I can only tell you about my own personal experiences. I was taking care of a beloved husband. You may be caring for a parent — or a wife or a daughter or a son — under very different conditions. But from whatever I have to offer, take what you need, modify it if that's better for you, and perhaps let me be for you the big sister I wished for.

Jim was a public face and, yes, that did in some ways make it easier. In other ways, it was very difficult. Living a life in the public eye has never been easy. His physical changes, seen by all, added unimaginable layers to the pain. Just managing to get a little much needed privacy was the trickiest of all. On the other hand, you may have to cope with problems and dilemmas that are entirely out of my scope. We all have our own unique perspective and our shared humanity. I can only give you what I have learned.

I offer you this with hope and my very best wishes.

Chapter Two

HOLD ON TIGHT

- Pin back all wires and cords.
- Have wrought iron banisters installed outside wherever needed.
- Walk downstairs in front of him — backwards if you can.
- Walk upstairs behind him.
- Sneak a little kiss on the back of his neck when you reach the top.
- Take his arm as usual, but this time, let him lean on you.

HOLD ON TIGHT

We never had live-in help — in the beginning because we couldn't afford it, and later because we loved our rarely achieved moments of privacy. So even after Jimmy got Parkinson's, we continued our three-times-a-week schedule with dear Sarah, who cleaned, did the laundry, and cooked us a little something.

We have a two-story house and the stairs were a major concern. So were the bathtub and the shower. The curved staircase terrified Jim and almost panicked me. I used to walk down a curved staircase backward in front of Jim as he climbed down, one hand on the banister and one clutching me. Walking down a curved staircase backwards wasn't easy. (If this were a movie, I would have received a stunt check!) When we went upstairs, he was in front of me, and as we reached the top, I would slide out and make a mad dash for the newel post to give him a final pull up. There had to be a better way!

Even when he was well, Jimmy loved to relax in the tub — which was fine and very good therapy at any time. He used to soak happily with his fish and his duck and his sailboat, and sometimes me. Once he got sick we decided, after several attempts in the shower, that the tub would be easier on both of us. The shower, even with the best non-skid rubber mat and my arms holding him up, presented too much of a hazard. Although I was strong, supporting a tall, broad, slippery man was hardly safe.

So one day we returned to the tub, and it was wonderful! There we were, sharing a bubble bath, wallowing in all that warm frothy water. I was the first to clamber out. Jim proceeded to follow. Suddenly, with his left leg hanging out of the tub and his right leg in, he froze. He couldn't move. He commanded his brain to move his legs, but nothing happened. He panicked.

"Get me out of here!" he yelled.

I rushed over to help. We tried together. I pushed and he pulled, but his legs were hopelessly locked. So I wrapped a bath towel around myself, dashed downstairs, unlocked the front door, and then telephoned the private patrol. Somehow their dispatcher, in addition to sending two of our patrol cops, also alerted the fire department, which sent a screaming fire engine. It came shrieking up our driveway and suddenly, staring at me in my towel and Jimmy sitting helplessly in the tub, stood the uniformed patrols and two brawny firemen in full regalia. I was terrified that our dispatcher might have also alerted the press. I had to find a better solution.

Suddenly, right in the midst of all the tub turmoil, a bulb lit up in my head. "I got it! Handles! That would do it!" I remembered that years ago, when I was in the hospital, they had grab bars on either side of the toilet. So I had handles put in — strong, secure handles — on either side of the toilet, the tub, on three sides of the shower, and all the way down the wall opposite the staircase. They would have been a blessing years ago when I broke my foot. Actually, they should be standard equipment in every building.

Everything worked perfectly, except the shower. It was better than nothing, but the handles would get slippery, too. So I found another solution. I figured that if I took his walker, which he refused to use anyway, and put it in the shower, he could hang onto it and even lean on it. It was perfect. Try it. Be sure the shower mat is in perfect condition and clamped down in just the right spot. We started to use the walker in there regularly and, with some soap and a little help from me, away we went!

I had heavy wrought iron railings put on either side of the pool, too. If you have a pool, use it, but not unless your patient is a swimmer and you are a hell of a good one, yourself. Otherwise, leave it to the physical therapist. Most of them arrange for time in a pool for their patients as that's about the most perfect exercise they can have.

Jim and I have been swimming all of our lives, but the first few times he tried after he became ill, he clung to the sides and "locked." After a number of tries, he finally got his courage back and was able to swing it. Much later, and in Jim's case it took quite a few attempts, he was able to swim fairly well. Before Jim got sick, we used to "race" and play "Olympics" in the water. With Parkinson's we still did it, but in the shallow end and across the width of the pool.

If you know what you are doing and have access to a pool, it's a godsend. Your doctor will advise you of Parkinson's care therapists, most of whom have access to a pool at no additional charge. But in any case, discuss this with your therapist. Even if she advises against actually swimming, she may give the patient a set of water exercises. They'll be wonderful for the patient, and they won't hurt you a bit!

We live in California, where a pool is as much a part of the scenery as our palm trees. Nearly everyone has a pool or has access to one. Just about all the apartment houses, schools, and public buildings have pools that can be heated in winter. We never stop swimming out here.

Recently a young friend of mine who worked in the office at St. John's Hospital said with much excitement, "I've been looking for place to live for ages. I'm living at home in the valley, and that's too far away from my job. But everything is so expensive on the west side. Well, today I think I found the right one. I'm so thrilled!" she bubbled. "It's one of the older apartment houses in Santa Monica. I overlook the garden, and I've got a living room, a bedroom, a kitchen, a dinette, and a lovely balcony."

Knowing that Santa Monica was one of our most desirable areas, I asked her if she could afford it.

"That's the best part," she said. "It's a sublet! The people who had it are being transferred to London, and they're letting me have it all furnished for what they pay, and it's still under the rent control ceiling!"

I was very happy for her. What a break!

My young friend called a week later. She

amazed me by asking if I knew of anything to rent in nearby Westwood.

"What happened to the great apartment you were supposed to take a week ago?!"

"Oh," she pouted. "I had to turn that down. I found out it didn't have a pool."

As a final note, let me add that the pool should be heated to about ninety degrees all year 'round. Ours is so hot that Jim said, "If you swim with a matzah ball in your mouth you'll get exercise and nourishment at the same time!" The gas bill and the pool maintenance are a very expensive proposition, so I don't advise a private pool unless your nest egg is Fabergé.

Chapter Three

"FOOD GLORIOUS FOOD"

- Half-fill his cup or glass.
- Be sure the glass is plastic and slip-proof.
- Make him wonderful, nutritious drinks between meals.
- Give him one or two not-so-nutritious drinks before dinner — perhaps one to sleep on at bedtime.
- Put a flower on his tray.
- Give him rather small portions.
- Praise him when he asks for seconds.
- Tell him he's wonderful.

"FOOD GLORIOUS FOOD"

When it came to feeding Jimmy, I tried hard to maintain an even keel. I had always loved to cook. I considered it an art and a pleasure. I made a study of it. So when we were first married Jimmy had no excuse to do any of the "bride's burnt biscuit" jokes. He could never have said that ours was the only garbage disposal unit in the world that had to take bicarbonate of soda, or that Aborigines came every year to dip their darts in my stew.

But it took him a long time to get used to my idea of a meal, because when it came to food, Jimmy was originally from that part of the country where green vegetables were thought of as a Communist plot.

But all that changed and I no longer had to say "Num, num, look at Mommy eat it. It's good!"

Once Jim got sick, I had to cut my time in the kitchen. With Jim always in another part of the house, I found that I'd be in the middle of the trickiest part of a dish when he would suddenly call for help, and of course, all would be ruined!

On Monday, Wednesday and Friday, when Sarah came to help me, she would make one of her marvelous dishes that could be relished twice. On the second go 'round I would change it. If, for instance, she made a stew for Monday night, on Tuesday when I was without help, I would turn the leftovers into a curry and serve it with rice and a few of the little side dishes to be added during the meal, like chopped peanuts, chutney, chopped raw apple, or whatever. Or perhaps I'd shred the meat and add a can of drained kidney beans and some chile powder and a clove of garlic or two. And voila. Mexico!

On the few occasions when Sarah was unavailable, I had my trusty crock pot. I could put any long-cooking dish into it in the morning, leave it on low all day, and at six-thirty or so that evening there it was — ready! Dishes like that, with a salad and a simple desert, took very little time away from Jimmy, and they didn't demand that I stay glued to the kitchen if and when I was needed elsewhere.

I was lucky because Jim had a very good appetite throughout his illness, and he was always a pleasure to feed. The doctors suggested that I give him one or two drinks before dinner to relax him and perk up his appetite. Of course, each patient's condition and treatment is unique. Although Jim's doctors encouraged him to drink alcohol as part of his treatment, I urge you to consult your patient's doctor before serving alcoholic beverages to any seriously ill person.

As Jimmy's doctors recommended alcohol, I learned to make his favorite drink, a mai-tai. The first few times I made it, it took more time than the dinner. I used various fresh fruits, and I juiced them myself. I actually picked the oranges off our very own tree. This drink had to be as good as the ones made by Jim's favorite bartender in our favorite Chinese restaurant — or else! But Jimmy, who drank every drop anyway, kept finding just a little gentle fault with each one. So the next time we went to "Madam Wu's," I told the bartender my problem. He said "That's not the way *I* make them! You're going to too much trouble! Look!" He pulled out a bottle of rum and a bottle of a commercial mix, and all he did was follow the directions on the back of the mix bottle — And it was great! I've tried several of the mixes. I have yet to hit one that wasn't better than all my fussing with a lot of fresh fruit!

On occasion, after dinner I would make Jimmy his other favorite drink, a stinger! "Henny's are the best," he would expound. (Let me tell you just one little secret. Jimmy had no idea what went on in a kitchen. He could cook nothing and never had the slightest desire to try. He would occasionally wander in there and look around in amazement as if to say, "I wonder what this room is for.") Of course, my stingers were great. An idiot can make them. It's just brandy and mint. I use Feffermint Schnapps because it's the driest. And a fine cognac. A stinger is only as good as your two ingredients.

Now for the nutritious drink. For the basic drink, put a tumbler full of ice cubes into your blender with an equal amount of water. Give it a spin, just until the ice is crushed. Now add four level tablespoons of powdered unsweetened cocoa, and two teaspoons of sugar or the sweetener equivalent. You can adjust that at the end to suit his taste. Add a cap of either vanilla or rum flavoring, whichever pleases him. Now add at least a half-cup of powdered milk. I used non-fat milk. The more powdered milk you add, the foamier, frothier, and more delicious it will be. I made it ahead of time, as I did most of the dinner, to get it out of the way of my other chores. If you do so, then put it in the fridge in the blender container. When you take it out, give it another whirl to fluff it up before you serve it. To this drink I often add one or two bananas (in which case you might omit the sugar) or a couple of skinned, pitted peaches. Another version is to omit the cocoa and vanilla or rum and just do the ice cubes and water, then add a tumbler of orange juice and powdered milk to taste. Remember "Orange Julius" and their top security secret recipe? You've just made one!

One day our agent called us about doing the Joanne Carson cooking show. Joanne was Johnny's second wife. They requested that we "dress" it, as this one would be the deciding program for a possible pickup, and the sponsors would be watching. Jim was his elegant self, and I wore a magnificent gold caftan.

Tape day arrived and we were all in fine fettle. The show went steaming along. Now it was time for me to make a little something to titillate the palate. I had elected to make our low calorie chocolate drink. The cameras came in tight on the three of us, very close on me with Joanne and Jim leaning over each shoulder. I put into the blender four tablespoons of cocoa, two packets of sweetener, a tumbler of ice cubes, two tumblers of water, a cap of vanilla, and three-quarters of a cup of powdered skim milk, when Joanne cried, "Oh, let *me* turn it on." And, forgetting all about the lid, she reached in and pushed the button. We stood there with our mouths open in amazement as the chocolate mess flew up, went all over the set, and covered we three fools from head to foot with the best chocolate drink you ever tasted.

The audience howled while we tried to get all of that thick brown mess out of our hair, our eyes, and our clothes, while the cameras rolled on and on and on. There was no need for retakes. The sponsors loved it and the show was picked up.

Along with all the other ready-to-eat or made ahead timesaving food in your fridge, be sure you always have little bowls of Jell-O and stewed dried fruit, especially prunes. And, of course, baked apples stuffed with raisins and walnut bits. Keep lots of juices handy for any emergency, especially prune juice, about which I promise not to tell you any stale jokes, like the one about the latest drink. It's made of prune juice and vodka. It's called a "Hurry Mary."

Chapter Four

EASY DOES IT

- Fluff his pillow.
- Leave a little note beside him when he's napping.
- Put a peppermint on his pillow.
- Fluff it up again.
- Don't hover.
- Throw him a kiss.

EASY DOES IT

My poor Jimmy. Not once during the first four years of his illness was he comfortable in bed. He couldn't climb in, slide up or down, turn over, or even sit up without being hoisted. And all night long, up to the bathroom with all that entailed, then back to bed, hoisted.

Sitting up wasn't so bad. He had been for some years the voice of La-Z-Boy chairs, so they had naturally sent him one. Any of those commercial recliners are more than satisfactory. I actually grew up in a household with a genuine "Morris" chair, so I was an old hand at this. I got him some pillows to use on any other chairs and to take along with him in the car. One was a triangular back pillow, and we had three little, round, very firm cylindrical ones to put in different places, on which I sewed heavy ribbon handles to make them easier to carry. You have no idea what a help they are.

But the bed. He was really miserable and kept complaining about it. Who had a better right?

I thought somehow that he would get used to it, as he got used to so many really uncomfortable situations, to say nothing of unwieldy outfits. I remember when Jim was playing the centurion, which is the Roman version of a top sergeant, to Victor Mature's captain in the movie of George Bernard Shaw's *Androcles and the Lion*. This was an especially tough assignment because, to begin with, Jim had to get up at dawn to be in makeup at 6:30 to have his hair curled. Then it took a full hour for three wardrobe men to get him into the authentic Roman armor. First they put on those sandals with the straps that wound around his legs up to his knees. Then came a suede T-shirt, followed by a shirt made of long heavy leather strips studded with chunks of iron, under which he wore flesh-colored panties, for obvious reasons. Over this went a chemise made of steel chains, which were gathered in by a belt, and from his shoulders hung a long, green, plush "Lowe's Pitkin Theatre" curtain. On both arms he wore classical butchers' cuffs of cowhide, in which were stashed two daggers. To top all this off, there was a helmet with a crazy ponytail down the back. When they first put this helmet on him, it was so heavy he blacked out. So they had to line it with sponge rubber. For accessories he held a gnarled club in his left hand and a spear in his right. Now mind you, he was only a sergeant, so you can imaging what they hung on Mr. Mature!

Jim wore that costume in this movie for four months — every day, all day long — until he was pushed and pulled and propelled back into his dressing room at the end of the day. What he wanted to know was how the Roman soldiers ever managed to pillage in that outfit. He couldn't even go to the men's room. But he and Vic got used to them. Sometimes they even went off the lot for lunch all done up like that. After a while they got so used to the whole thing they thought nothing of it.

I was hoping that that would be the case with his bed problems. But no such luck. One day I saw an ad for an electric adjustable bed, like they have in hospitals. It was a wonder and changed everything. Now we couldn't get him out of it! I once asked George Burns how he stayed so young. What was his secret? He replied, "Don't fall in love with your bed." I guess he didn't have one of those adjustable beds.

Talk to your doctor about this. If you are over sixty-five, and have your doctor's say-so, your Medicare may pay for it. Also, some insurance polices may cover this.

Another thing that drove Jim crazy was shoes. Everything hurt, until I found those soft bedroom slippers with the woolly lining and non-slip, non-skid soles. He adored them. We had to chain him to the house to prevent his sneaking out with these on his feet. I'm sure had he still been playing golf, he would have put spikes put on them!

Chapter Five

PUTTING ON THE MOVES

- Take walks with him.
- Do his physical exercises with him.
- Have pretend Olympic races across the pool — widthwise.
- Make a game of everything.
- Try to let him do some things alone.
- Hug him.
- Keep calm.

PUTTING ON THE MOVES

When we first appeared at physical therapy, Becki, our therapist, showed us some exercises that are done in tandem. She guaranteed that they would be very helpful to Jim, and wouldn't do me a bit of harm! Exercising by yourself is a lonely business. With me along for the moves, it would be much easier on Jim. We did these faithfully at home on his non-physical therapy clinic days.

These exercises were designed for strengthening and coordination and consisted of turns and many stretches. We had to plan our space ahead, as Parkinson's people must of necessity do very wide turns. Everything is done super-slowly. We were lucky in our space at home because we had an extra safety handle in our exercise room and it became our ballet barre. It took a lot of loving persuasion to get this patient moving. He reluctantly did all of the exercises — only because he was not alone — but this wasn't tops on his hit parade.

I mentioned swimming, which is just about the best exercise ever. Do not forget, unless you are a really strong swimmer, and you have the blessing of your doctor, stay out! If you do not have access to a pool, there *is* help. And don't forget, it is always a good idea to call your doctor for guidance and information.

When Jim was young he had a tough decision to make; would he become an actor or a professional golfer? He had been a child golf champion and later was the fourth best "A" golfer around. Before he got sick, he used to hit plastic golf balls in our yard. But now he found it difficult to make the turn required for a golf swing. And what was even worse, it made him dizzy. It isn't much fun for the patient, and it could even prove to be dangerous. But putting is fine. You can do that anywhere. All you need is a putter, a ball, and an old hat to putt into.

Though Jim found golf, his beloved game, too difficult to manage, this may not be so with your patient. As proof of this point, let me relay to you this piece of information which just came to me in a brochure this year:

"The Houston Area Parkinson's Society (HAPS) holds a golf tournament in April, Parkinson's Awareness Month. The tournament is open to all golfers, of all ages, who have Parkinson's disease. The Houston Area Parkinson Society Golf Club has shown that Parkinson's golfers can play regularly in a relaxed, no-rush environment."

If a "no-rush" golf club is not easily available to you, I am sure that if the patient is able to play golf he will enjoy hitting a bucket of balls. I've never known a golfer who didn't love to practice.

Golf was what Jim missed most. Or was it acting? To an actor, any day that you don't act is a wasted day. As Lord Laurence Olivier said, "Acting is a kind of masochistic form of exhibitionism. It was born in me and I don't seem to be able to stop."

This must be true of many callings, and with an illness like this, what can we give our patients to replace it?

Jim's favorite of all the prescribed activities was dancing, or what passed as such. Just letting go to music to the best of his ability. I would put on the music — some of his favorites, songs we had once danced to — and he would do a few loosening up exercises and then move to the beat. We called this "dancing for Mommy." Remember when you were little and totally without inhibitions, and when the music played you just did whatever came naturally, and you said, "Look, Mommy, I'm dancing?" That's all there is to it, and it's the best.

At first there were a lot of problems getting him to do this, with all the accompanying "I cant's." But at last, the music got to him and away he went. It was such a success that sometimes when we were just walking along minding our own business, he would throw in a little "dance for Mommy" just for the hell of it.

Before I end this chapter, I have to say a word about the number-one activity for all the Parkinson's patients — walking! If the secret is exercise, exercise, exercise, then where walking is concerned, enough is never enough!

Chapter Six

WORRY, BARYSHNIKOV!

- Dance around the room and encourage him to join in.
- Play his favorite music, even if it's rock.
- Ask him to show you how he used to dance for Mommy.
- Keep him laughing.
- Tell him he's the cutest.

WORRY, BARYSHNIKOV!

When Jimmy first got sick, his doctor told him that the secret was to exercise, exercise, exercise. "And remember, Jim," he added, "this disease, for which there is as yet no cure, can be controlled. That is, if you exercise and take your medication."

This was told to us in 1978, when there was very little in the way of medication. Mostly it was a pill that contained a lot of L-Dopa, that substance that's supposed to bring back the Dopamine to your brain. At that time, L-Dopa was the rage with the anything-for-a-kick set. It was said to be a well-documented fact that L-Dopa aroused you sexually. It's street worth was twenty-five bucks a pill. By that reckoning, Jim, with his bottle full of it, was some kind of millionaire!

That much-touted arousal? Well, let's not believe everything we hear. Not once did Jim pursue me from room to room like the centerfold of the Kama Sutra. He was hardly the recipient of an L-Dopa-induced satyriasis. It was about as much sexual help as ginseng root or ground up rhino horn.

Good patient that he was, Jim took his medication and he exercised. He tried everything that was listed in the Parkinson's rehabilitation manual. Three times a week he went to a physical therapist where he got a workout with strange contraptions. The huge room was filled with chairs, tables, and slant boards oozing with wires, chains and straps. It looked like the rumpus room of the Marquis de Sade. After his workout, however, he was rewarded by a cheerful man who massaged, kneaded, and soothed his muscles and tendons in the never-ending race against Dr. Parkinson and his forces of evil.

The real secret was to keep moving, and moving every part of the body. "Jogging!" I exclaimed. "That will do it." He hated the thought, but I talked him into it, Or rather, I lured him with Adidas running shoes, a stop watch, and one of those big earmuff radios to keep him abreast of the news. He hated it. So he switched to walking. He did it every day and loved it. Whatever works, as they say.

What he needed, we figured, in addition to everything else, was more stretching. And what was the best for that? Ballet, of course. Like most actors who go to drama school, Jim had taken singing, fencing, and some dancing lessons. And like most actors, he saw nothing wrong with trying ballet. If your patient balks and thinks it's "sissy," just mention Baryshnikov and his two children by his lady love. Or tell him about Ballenchine and his five marriages to the most beautiful of ballerinas. And tell him about that young man named Patrick Swayze. Ever see a more masculine dancer? Oh, well, of course let's not forget Gene Kelly. Masculine? No one would ever have dared to tell Gene Kelly that what he was doing was "sissy!"

So Jimmy went to ballet class and he loved it. All that stretching and turning helped like nothing else. Here again, discuss it with your doctor. Some patients may be more comfortable with yoga. And be sure of the teacher's credentials. Often a physical therapist can recommend a ballet teacher who has had experience in working with Parkinson's patients.

Oh, and be sure to tell your husband that every ballet studio has a barre!

Chapter Seven

SING, SING, SING A LITTLE SOMETHING

- Sing to him — even if you can't sing.
- Have him do his tongue and vocal exercises into a little recorder.
- Learn the lyrics to his song — school, love, or pornographic.

SING, SING, SING A LITTLE SOMETHING

Once on "Hollywood Squares" the question was, "Who is the second most identifiable voice in the world?" The answer: "Jim Backus." Now you are wondering who was the first most identifiable voice in the world. It turned out to be an unidentified Imam who called the Moslem world to prayer — on tape!

Jim's greatest fear was a diminished voice. It was also very important for him to be audible for my sake. (I have a hearing problem, which may be a besetting factor in your case, too.) Here, once again, what is of the greatest importance is exercise, exercise, exercise! At least exercising his voice is pure fun!

Did you ever hear of anybody who didn't love to sing in the shower, the tub, the bathroom, or whatever? Who doesn't love to sing? I am beginning to think this is *really* everyone's number one private fantasy! Or, to get up there and belt out a little number like Barbra Streisand, or croon a tune like Frank Sinatra, or maybe opera, like Pavarotti? Well, sure! But I don't think you'll have any trouble getting your patient to do a little singing.

I started to sneak up on Jim by singing in the car. Pretty soon, he joined in. It soon became standard for us to get into the car and burst into song. I knew it would alleviate some of his anxieties as we rode forth to yet another doctor.

Singing is a kind of magic! Jim was advised to get a vocal therapist, which we did — the wonderful Carolyn Trojanovski, who came every week to go through their exercises and work on a song. He loved it.

Our doctor insisted that Jim take vocal lessons, which he claimed would be beneficial to any Parkinson's patient. Everything is exercised — the tongue, the jaw, and the entire breathing apparatus. I have always found vocal lessons very difficult. It takes a lot of stamina. You have to work with someone who is a most experienced teacher and who has had a real background working with Parkinson's patients. Don't fool around with this one. You know where to go for help. Your primary physician is always your number one resource!

Jim and I worked on his singing voice every chance we got. Maybe because we were actors, it seemed like the natural thing to do. We had a little tape recorder into which we sometimes sang duets. One of our routines was pretending to be a latter day Mills Brothers group. Jim would sing the melody, very carefully enunciating the lyrics, as Carolyn insisted he do, while I would do the rhythmic bass accompaniment. I would start to vamp, — Boom! — Boom! — Boom! Then Jim would join in with the melody as I boomed underneath. I guess I was the only singing wife whose voice was lower than her husband's! Don't knock it. A singing patient is a happy patient.

Along with the vocal lessons came an exercise that I would have loved to watch, if only

Jim had let me. It was face making. Making faces before a mirror helps to maintain the mobility of the facial muscles. All the muscles will come into play if the patient will smile, snarl, grin, pout, whistle and puff out his cheeks. Tell him to do this whenever he passes a mirror — oh, sure he will! But it is sort of fun, and he should do this several times a day. If he resists, try making a game out of it by engaging him in spontaneous face-making contests. It will exercise the muscles and lift the spirits for both of you!

We also acted. We played scenes into the little tape recorder. Isn't everyone a frustrated actor? It was great. We took roles they never would have assigned to us. I would be, perhaps, the very young ingenue in "Our Town," while Jim was the mother. We had the fun of playing it back, and perhaps even boring a few friends with our glorious performances. Some of these tapes were hilarious. I saved them, and, as anybody can hear, these tapes are not about show business; they are about the healing business.

With the tape recorder you can be anything. Have your patient do a newsman, like maybe Walter Cronkite. Just give him a newspaper, remind him to enunciate, and let him loose with that cassette player. Don't think this isn't helpful. What could be better for both of you than a patient who isn't grumpy or depressed or panicked or listless? There isn't room for that when you have a great performance to give.

Chapter Eight

BABYING HIM

- Don't be afraid to do the enemas yourself.
- Croon to him if he's frightened or embarrassed.
- Be patient — learn to wait.
- Try a little baby talk.
- Tell him he's wonderful.

BABYING HIM

The best things in life aren't things. They're hugs and kisses and love. Your patient needs to hear that cherished word, "Love." — not only from you, but from his family, his friends, the people he works with and pals with and plays golf with. He'll thrive on it. Tell him there's nothing wrong with a nice, acceptable World Series hug from another guy. In my family, everybody kissed everybody anyway. But in Jim's, a pat on the back was considered a sexual overture.

Most sick people need to be babied. However, some feel that it robs them of their independence. But Jim adored it. He wallowed in it. Since the appetite grows on what it is fed, you may find that your patient, like mine, never seems to get enough attention. I was so worried that I might be overdoing it, that I'd emasculate him. But here, too, you have to find your way. Just watch out! No fussing or hovering!

If you have to spoon feed him, do it. But kid it. Make playing baby funny. Keep it light. If he is difficult, your acting like a comic idiot will sometimes pull him out of it. This also goes for any of the necessary, not-so-savory chores you may be called upon to perform. Enemas, for one. You may both feel more comfortable here with the services of a nurse. Jimmy refused to have one. So I stayed on the job and, oddly enough, it brought us closer together.

Jim was never incontinent, as some patients are. Actually, he was just the opposite. He hated it so that it became very hard for me to keep playing our baby game. But, like everything else, you do it and you get used to it, and finally you simply don't give it a thought. If your patient has difficulty urinating, put a heating pad on his stomach. If you feel that's too chancy, help him to the bathroom and put a hot water bag on his stomach while he waits to void, or try running water in the sink. Sometimes it takes a while. Put a radio beside him so he doesn't get bored or anxious. Be patient. If you are, he will be too. And if he's embarrassed or cranky, sooner or later he'll begin to understand your position and his fuming will ease up.

Try to get him to exercise his hands. A squeeze ball is boring. Get a soft rubber ball and play catch with him. Do it indoors if you have to. Just don't throw it too far. This, much to our surprise, was really great fun, and very good for his coordination. When the weather was good we took our catch game outdoors, but again we restricted it to a very small area. Naturally, I was the retriever. It was good for him to throw and catch, but chasing the ball was my job. Oh well, in for a nickel, in for a dime.

How about a little art? Jim turned me down cold. "I have no talent. Couldn't care less. Don't bother me." So I bought him a kids painting set — just a sketch pad and some acrylic paints — and left it lying around. Surprisingly enough, after ignoring them for ages, one day I found him curled over the pad, completely fascinated. He made marvelous cartoons for everybody and ended up doing lovely water colors. Try it! You may have a Utrilla in your villa.

When he's lying around, read to him. Everybody loves to be read to. For most of us it is a lovely, early memory.

Hold him. Cuddle him. I used to hold Jimmy tight all through the night. I honestly believed that if I held him tight enough, my energy would flow into him and make him well. I'm sad to say it didn't make him well. But it did make him better.

Chapter Nine

"YOU GOTTA HAVE HEART"

- Buy him relaxation tapes, perhaps of ocean waves or rain.
- Massage his neck.
- Massage his back.
- Massage all of him.
- Stand by — but subtly.

"YOU GOTTA HAVE HEART"

My husband was the world's champion hypochondriac. If they had an Olympic event for it, he would have gotten the gold. The heads of our Hollywood charities had a great pigeon in Jimmy. He was in constant demand to emcee their benefits. He loved to do them, and why not? Then he would come home with whatever disease they were plugging, and it was his big chance to regale me with its symptoms. I was used to that and had long ago found ways to kid him out of it.

But now he had Parkinson's disease. It was real. It had a handle. He suffered from terrible depression, especially in the beginning. For some reason these attacks always seemed to occur on Sunday, when we were entirely alone. Jimmy, the world's greatest chain talker, would clam up and lie in bed like a stone, staring straight ahead. I couldn't stand it when he got like that. He seemed so lost. No matter what I did, all he wanted was that mattress and to be left alone. Not even soft conversation could lure him up.

When I could finally get him out of that bed, out of his pajamas, and — Hallelujah! — standing up, the battle was half won. "Make him move," they would tell me. "Make him exercise! Make him walk!"

By the time he was ready to walk, I was ready for bed. But, again, if it happens to you, I beg of you, don't give up. After once having arisen and exercised, he sometimes would forget the whole thing. He seemed to have no memory of having been in that terrible state just a short time ago.

Sometimes it was so rough, I was afraid that I had bitten off more than I could chew. But when he finally smiled at me, I knew it was a great mouthful. So do keep up the good fight. Your strength will come.

Jim also suffered from occasional panic. This was nothing new. He had periods of this throughout his life and had been in and out of treatment for years. Currently, he was in. Psychotherapy can be an expensive business, but there are many very good clinics.

It's often not the long, involved treatment it once was. Today they get right to the point. Sometimes when Jim was especially wiped out, he and his therapist would do his session over the telephone, a very usual occurrence.

We amassed a number of spiritual and relaxation books and tapes. Some we bought, but most of them were sent by his marvelous, concerned fans. Many of these were of great help.

When he felt an attack coming on, he would immediately lie down, get as comfortable as he possibly could, and listen to a tape. More often than not, it would relax him and prevent the attack. It took some sifting and listening to find the best, most helpful ones.

Sometimes his attacks would rub off on me. *Then* where would we be? Disaster time! So I would lie down and listen to the tapes too. I also had my back log of years of hypnosis. Now there are also support groups. Once again, please talk to your doctor.

Many people have strange and distorted ideas of what hypnosis really is. Hypnosis is an altered state of consciousness whereby the subconscious is more available to suggestion. The subconscious is a "helper" and can learn to assist the person who is hypnotized. Being "under" is a most wonderful feeling of utter relaxation. Anyone who wants to can be hypnotized, but if you fight it, forget it. The hypnosis subject is always in charge. You can come out of the trance yourself whenever you wish to. And if you practice this, sooner or later you will be able to hypnotize yourself at will. I have found self-hypnosis to be one of my most valuable tools.

I am also lucky to have a great coping mechanism, which is now called "denial." This is where you refuse to see what you don't want to see. It sustained me. That and the fact that I, too, listened to those relaxation tapes. Most of the time this small treatment worked for both of us. And the sun broke through the clouds.

Many people have no idea how difficult it can be to care for someone with a serious illness. You have to work awfully hard to make it look easy.

Chapter Ten

BEWARE OF HISSY FITS!

- If he has a tantrum and screams at you, make light of it and kiss his pointing finger.
- Be his best friend — even on those days when he seems to have stopped being yours.
- Keep it light.
- Try to anticipate him.
- Hang on to your sense of humor.

BEWARE OF HISSY FITS!

My husband had the disposition of an angel. He bore what had to be borne with great grace. Only twice in the ten-and-a-half years of his illness do I remember his having what Carol Burnett's grandmother used to call a "hissy fit." But when he had one, he did it right — with all the required yelling and stamping of the feet. (Wait a minute! How did he get his brain to telegraph "stamping" right on cue like that? Patients can do mysterious things sometimes. It's a puzzlement.)

I remember the first fit only too well. I never saw such a performance, and all because he couldn't undo the double knot I had tied in his shoelaces to keep them from coming apart and tripping him. I tried to get through to him. I even tried to help him untie them. I tried to explain. But he simply couldn't hear me through all that noise he was making.

The second fit occurred because he couldn't fold back his newspaper page. I saw him struggling with it. No matter how he tried, it just kept crumpling and driving him crazy. He even gave me a smart smack on the hand when I attempted to help him. I couldn't blame him. That crinkling and crackling of the paper was enough to drive anyone crazy. It's hard enough even when you're functioning perfectly to manage turning those obstinately unwieldy newspaper pages. But that, plus the other maddening frustrations of a Parkinson's patient's day, sent him into this giant tantrum.

It was especially hard for him to realize at the beginning of his illness that I was merely trying to help, that I was trying to find *my* way too. It took a while for him to understand that I wasn't going to smother him and that I was not ever going to hover. It wasn't easy to hit a happy medium. But I was patient with the patient. You be patient with yours, too. And don't worry about it. Remember, all in good time.

He liked me to arrange my day so that I could lie down with him when he took his nap. I loved that, too. And sometimes when I was really tired I would lie beside him when he was watching television. But drifting off to sleep was impossible with all that sound. Finally, through a dear friend and a bit of luck, I came across something wonderful. It's a wireless head set that attaches to your television. You can turn down the sound to where it is virtually off. Then I could fall asleep or read if I cared to while Jimmy could hear perfectly through the little ear muffs. He loved it — he had a defective ear anyway! He said it was perfectly clear and he could now hear better than ever. And as for me, I saved up for it and gave it to him as a gift. They are around a hundred dollars, and may I say it was the best buy I ever made. It was a hell of a lot better than listening to yet another golf lesson or tournament or, heaven forbid, a football game! One more of those and I would have had a hissy fit of my own!

When he was really sweet and began to understand what I was trying to do, I would reward him, with the doctor's permission of course, with an extra drink before dinner. But you have to watch that. I'm sure you don't want your patient to wake up the next morning with what Robert Mitchum used to call, "a bad case of brewer's flu."

Chapter Eleven

STAYING HOME IN STYLE

- Get in the tub with him.
- Before his nap give him a beer in a light mug with a handle.
- Be sure he's sitting down when he pulls on his trousers.
- Tell him he's adorable.
- Let him shine whenever he can.

STAYING HOME IN STYLE

Unless we were familiar with the surroundings, we had to turn down quite a few parties once Jim became ill. One was held in a house whose front door had miles of stairs leading to it, but no railings. Another had rooms on different levels and, once again, with nothing Jim could grab onto. My husband — the gregarious one who loved people, who loved to entertain, who loved to be entertained — missed so many evenings he would have enjoyed. He adored getting up at one of our Hollywood gatherings and telling his ridiculously funny stories. Parkinson's cheated him out of the chance to get back his feeling of self worth, to be back in the swim, to be what he was programmed to be — an entertainer.

I caught myself once recollecting all the fun we used to have at parties, especially our own. All kinds — birthday parties, garden parties, New Year's Eves, barbecues — especially barbecues! No wonder. Jimmy's steaks were very good. For charcoal he used the steaks he barbecued the night before!

But enough! I realized I was wallowing in an orgy of nostalgia. So finally I decided to try a party of our own. It took planning and a lot of organization, but it can be done! You can do it! It doesn't have to be big or fancy. Start with a few friends for an informal, simple dinner. I started that way, but as time went on, the party grew. Finally I found myself doing black tie, sit down dinners for twelve. It worked. He enjoyed them so! However, I did need some help for those.

To me the worst thing about giving a party is that period after everything is primed and ready, waiting for your guests to arrive. I had to spare Jimmy from hosting duty. Since he was the star of the evening, and everyone knew he was not too well, it was easily finessed — I would call the evening for seven o'clock, with dinner at eight-thirty and, when all were assembled, he would make his appearance. This gave everyone a flexible arrival time and, once Jim came down, a full cocktail hour in which he could shine. This system worked well, because the after-dinner period was, of necessity, a short one. When I saw him starting to fade, our guests would get a silent cue from me and begin to gracefully drift out. Since most people are sensitive to such situations, they always played this scene beautifully. And I was left with a happy camper.

NOTES

Chapter Twelve

GOING OUT IN STYLE

- Give him a pillow roll and put one in the car, too.
- Be sure his window is partly open if you have to leave him alone in the car.
- Protect him from drafts.
- Order food that needs no cutting.

GOING OUT IN STYLE

When you are about to take a Parkinson's patient out to a restaurant, the most important thing to determine is whether they have parking and, if not, where do you go? If they had no valet parking and the restaurant was unfamiliar to me, I always took a trip well in advance of our due date to case it. Was there parking close by? Was it safe? Would it be hard to maneuver? Was the sidewalk or curb broken or cracked or uneven? Would it have to be street parking? Is there a sign that says, "Permit Parking Only?" Will it be well lighted?

We tried to patronize those old restaurants that we had known for many years, like Chasen's, The Bistro, Madame Wu's and one wonderful neighborhood place called The Brentwood Inn. These were all fairly close by. All but the Brentwood Inn had valet parking; at the Brentwood Inn the closest place to park your car could be as much as an entire block away — all of that distance with cracked and broken curbs. The way we managed was to call the Brentwood Inn ahead and tell them when we would arrive. They were always sweet enough to have someone waiting at the door to help me get Jim out of the car and escort him to the table as subtly as possible while I did the parking. (I found that most restaurants try to give this service.) Accomplishing all this subtly was important. It was tough on Jim because he was so visible. Of course you don't have to be a celebrity to be stared at, and it's hard to smile graciously through this embarrassment.

Sometimes it was almost impossible to get Jimmy out of the car. As he was trying to emerge and got halfway out, his muscles would lock and he would start to fall out head first. It was a symptom but a guaranteed laugh getter. I'd have to try to gather him up quickly or we might hear a chorus of, "Oh, look! Here comes Mr. Magoo! Look, kids, Mr. Magoo just fell out of his car head first! Isn't Mr. Magoo a funny fellow!" Sometimes being visible isn't much fun.

It's wise to have someone waiting to help the patient get in and out of the car. Getting in you have to watch his head, and be ready to push it down if he hasn't done so himself. Once Jim forgot to duck and got a slight concussion. And this, I might add, was long before he got sick!

In restaurants we patronized, he was well known by the management, so he felt secure and protected. On those occasions when we went to a less protective eating place, there were often fans who wanted his autograph or came over to our table merely to shake his hand. They were friendly, kind, and understanding, but once in a while there would be an over-enthusiastic admirer who would stand at our table and recite the plots of every show he had ever done. He even learned, while his food got cold, to take that, too, in his stride, and to be grateful that they still admired him, handicap and all.

Even if your patient's face is not well known, he is bound to run into friends and acquaintances, or simply friendly strangers who will come over to the table and offer their sympathy. We found that everyone was truly kind and interested. But, I warn you, on a bad day, if your patient is hungry or cranky, it may take a bit of tact and a lot of patience.

Always reserve a quiet, out-of-the-way table. If there are banquets, so much the better. If your patient orders food that needs cutting or buttering, switch plates and do it and then return it to him in one movement. It entails a lot less fussing that way.

It might be wise to dawdle over coffee until the other diners have left. Then your patient can be helped to the door without an audience while you go and fetch the car.

Dining out was an effort, but it was worth it. Most of the time we were happy to be in a restaurant having a tête-à-tête and some dinner in a cozy nook. Try it. It may seem like old times.

Chapter Thirteen

CUDDLE UP A LITTLE CLOSER

- Give him a massage with all the oils and unguents.
- Do the cologne and talcum powder ritual for him.
- Tuck a towel in the neck of his robe and tell him he looks sexy.
- Tell him he's your lord and master.
- Study the Kama Sutra.
- Use it!

CUDDLE UP A LITTLE CLOSER

I have a dear friend whose husband has recently been evaluated as having Parkinson's disease. They are newly married, and naturally, sex is of great concern to them.

"First things first," I told her. "Do you remember that unfunny joke we heard in high school? It ended with, "you get on top, let his mother worry.""

I don't recall its corny plot, which is just as well, but it has a mighty handy tag line. Tell your partner, first of all, not to fret. There are all sorts of areas to be explored. You couldn't have covered them all. If one doesn't work, another one will. Tell him that in any marriage things change anyway as time goes by. The important thing to remember is that love, affection and attention are what we all crave. We're all really alike, but our styles are different. Tell him not to feel that he is handicapped, that nothing will be drastically altered, that you love him and want him. This is where the "lord and master" enters in and so does the Kama Sutra, or its equivalent. Use it, and your imagination. Be patient. Be daring. Be imaginative. Audition any intriguing possibility. If it's manageable and possible and it works, keep it in.

Make it fun.
Keep it light.
Be inventive.
Above all, make do.

One night at a party, Natalie Schaffer, who played Jim's wife, Lovey, on *Gilligan's Island*, told a group of us that she once had a lover who trembled delightfully whenever he touched her. She thought it was her. Then she found out he had Parkinson's disease.

NOTES

Chapter Fourteen

BE PREPARED!

- Make lists and try to stick with them.
- Write things down.
- Use Post-It notes for reminders.
- Give him an emery board as a bookmark — it sticks!
- Give him a rubber band as a bookmark if it's a paperback.
- Keep a diary.
- Keep him laughing.

BE PREPARED!

Late one night, Jim had a very bad fall. My 911 call quickly brought the paramedics, who took him to the emergency room at U.C.L.A. The doctors there thought it was best to keep him overnight and suggested that he would be less agitated if I slept by his side on a little cot. He was restless and complained that he needed some of his things, so I rushed home and brought him his glasses, his toothbrush, a comb, some slippers and, as he requested, a crossword puzzle book and some pencils. (How he intended to swing that I never found out!) I also brought the book he was currently reading. That I could read to him. I also brought my own reading glasses, a little makeup kit, my toothbrush, a travel mirror and my necessary can of hair spray. I later kept mine as a future hospital kit, just in case.

Our house in California sometimes shakes a bit, sometimes a lot. We also get an occasional rainstorm, sometimes a flood. So I kept what I call my earthquake kit beside my bed and another one that I would leave every night near the front door before I went to bed. I also kept a third one permanently in the trunk of my car. The moment an earthquake starts, I go! Who knows whether it will be a little shake, an after-shock, or heaven forbid, a big one like we had in January, 1994. An earthquake never telegraphs its intentions, so we just get out — fast!

I know some experts recommend that you

stay inside when an earthquake happens. But because of the layout of our home, we felt safer in the car. Look at your own surroundings. Get disaster planning advice and plan how to handle an emergency. Research what agencies offer this service — the city or the county.

I never let the gas in my car get below half full. This is important. There may be a shortage of gasoline after a disaster of any sort.

Beside the bed and at the front door, I would leave a robe for each of us and slippers with non-skid soles. If there was not time to put anything on upstairs, we could grab those on the run. A hefty pair of slippers is necessary in case of broken glass.

In the permanent disaster case in the car I kept three separate kits — one for Jim, one for me, and a master kit. In Jim's little personal kit I had two pairs of shorts, two pairs of pajamas, two T-shirts, a pair of sneakers, three pairs of socks, his glasses, toothbrush, toothpaste, a brush, a comb, a box of tissues, a bar of soap and washcloth in a plastic case, a week's supply of his medication, and needed extra medication, and a jug of suppositories.

In my kit I had a travel mirror, makeup, hair spray, a comb and a brush, a bar of soap and a washcloth in a little plastic case like Jim's, tissues, my eyeglasses, a toothbrush, my medication, two pairs of panties, two pairs of socks, two bras, two pairs of pajamas and a can of talcum powder.

In the third kit, the master case, I had a very good flashlight, some extra batteries, an alarm clock, a wristwatch, a radio (in case the one in the car went off), a small address book, some cash in both single bills and change, two six-packs of juices, a few plastic glasses, some paper plates, a packet of rice crackers, a jar of peanut butter and one of jelly, and a case containing a can opener, a knife, and scissors. I changed the crackers and juices once a month and the medicines as often as needed. Since we are reading junkies I also kept a few paperback books and some crossword puzzles with the accompanying pens and pencils. All these things were comfortably assembled in the car with the three personal kits in it as well. It was not nearly as cumbersome as it might sound. I still had room in the trunk proper for a cane, some pillows, blankets and towels. I also had two safari lights to read by, should we have a long wait somewhere.

Let me tell you about those safari lights, which have often saved the day, or should I say, the night. They are designed to stand up and serve. They are battery operated and light a large section of a room. I have one or two in every room in the house. They are a godsend and helped to keep me serene, well, slightly serene, after "the big one" in 1994. They come from the hardware or sporting goods store and are relatively inexpensive.

Jim had long since left us when the 1994 disaster struck. I was alone. When it seemed to me to be safe to go back into that pitch black house in our powerless city, I was able to read with those lights while I listened to the reports as they came over the portable radio until the sun came up, and I dared to move around to evaluate the extent of the damage.

It's very important to familiarize yourself

and your patient with what to expect during an emergency. Despite our preparations, despite our discussions, despite our rehearsals, Jim became confused and stiffened up when we actually had one of our larger shakes. There was no electric power, and leading him to safety was a small miracle. I still remember trying to get him to move and, with my forked tongue, I heard myself say, "I know you can do it!" And somehow he did.

Please do not minimize any of this. The worst may never happen, but if it does, you will need all the preparation you can get. We used everything in the car trunk on four different occasions. We were protected on the two hospital excursions by the medics and ambulance. As for the two earthquakes, I honestly never thought we'd reach the wonderful automobile, but once safely inside, we turned on the beautiful lights and the glorious radio, snuggled into our heavenly blankets and pillows from the trunk, and settled down for the long wait. And, by the way, I had to replace the crackers and juices long before their due date.

NOTES

Chapter Fifteen

S.O.S.

- Make friends with a druggist who delivers.
- Play board games with him that are easy to handle.
- Play word games that need no props.
- Introduce him to a bird and a butterfly.
- Give him a kiss in passing.
- Tell him he's wonderful.

S.O.S.

It wasn't easy. The guidance I share with you was born out of years of pain and confusion and struggling to find the way. No one can really hand you a set of rules. Ultimately, it's entirely up to you. Once or twice I was so exhausted and hysterical that I laid into my darling patient and suffered the pangs of guilt for days afterward. Losing control that way was particularly upsetting because it took so little to throw Jim into a panic.

I couldn't really ask for more help than the part-time people I had in the house because the healing process was somehow stronger when Jim and I were alone — really alone. Jim loved it and so did I. Just sitting quietly in the garden with no one around, talking to the birds and watching the butterflies, would calm him way down.

The time may come, however, when you'll have to send out a call for extra help. Most people have family members they can call on when the going gets rough. I would certainly have asked mine for help, but they were thousands of miles away, and Jim's family was gone. Though we had no family, we did have friends. If you are not comfortable with asking friends for help, or if for any reason support is not available, ask your doctor for the name of a service that comes to your house and provides help in many crucial areas.

I was getting very tired. I could no longer drive at night. Nor could I climb endlessly up and down those stairs. I was just thumbtacked together.

What the hell, I was sixty-nine when Jim got sick in 1978; now I was deep into my seventies — a strong, healthy seventies — and I could cope with most of it. But it was getting up and down throughout the night to the bathroom, with all that was entailed, that did me in. That, and never really having a few moments to myself. The doctors said I had to have a little privacy, a breather here and there. In your own case, remember what I just said! Don't wait until you collapse. There *is* help at hand. It's important to take care of yourself.

On top of all that, we were writing another book — committed, with a deadline! I was just plain exhausted. Although I was beginning to forget to give him his medicine, driving erratically, and having dizzy spells, that book had to be written. It would never have been possible had it not been for the greatest assistant in the world, Kathy (now Dr.) Segal, who helped us through *Backus Strikes Back* in 1984 and *Forgive Us Our Digressions* in 1988. Writing these was the very best therapy in the world for Jimmy, and I loved it, too.

Nor would I have still been standing on my feet were it not for the help of two other dear friends, Fred Phillips, my hairdresser, and John Gose. They were sensational! They helped me in so many ways. The best part was letting me get peacefully dressed and ready when we occasionally got to go out. Then one or the other would give Jim his shower and get him arrayed while I had my private moment. Fred also came in once a week to cut Jim's hair, do his nails, and generally groom him. If it had not been for Freddy, Jimmy would have looked like Howard Hughes! Once again, if the grooming needs of your patient are impossible for you to handle, check with your doctor. You will be amazed at the wealth of information and resources that are just a phone call away!

This was fine, as far as it went, but I really needed more help. Then one terrifying incident became the deciding factor.

Most of our doctors were in the St. John's Hospital office building which, by California standards, is a high rise. Twelve stories up in the air. I hate heights — and all of our doctors were on the top floor.

I had to make myself get into that elevator and help Jimmy get up there. On this particular day we were alone in the elevator, which had reached the twelfth floor. As usual, I had gotten out and had Jim firmly by the arms ready to pull when, with one leg in the elevator and one leg out, he froze. He was riveted to the floor. There was no time to go around him and hit that hold button again. Besides, I didn't dare let go. I just pulled! Nothing! Suddenly, a hand shot out of nowhere and gave us a giant yank, which landed us both safely flat on the floor. Our champion leaped onto the descending elevator; he was gone. We were safe! We were grateful! We were lucky! We were stupid! Never, never, never get into an elevator without someone to help you get out.

The only plus that scare gave us was finding Ralph, the nephew of our housekeeper, Sarah. He was working nights in a building in nearby Westwood and was able to give us three afternoons a week. It was heaven! It revived me. Need I say it once again? Talk to your doctor. Whatever your needs are in that area, there is help available.

A new person can be as good for the patient as it is for the caretaker. At first Jim resented it. "How could you do this to me?" Then he got used to the new situation. It was a natural progression. Finally, he just loved having a man to talk to, especially when he found he had a new appreciative audience. And his "cup ranneth over" when Ralph took him to the golf tournament! Jimmy smiled more. He laughed more. He was happier.

And I was hurt. He doesn't miss me! He doesn't need me anymore!

Of course he missed me. Of course he needed me. He had simply begun to realize that this was the better way. If you get someone to help you and your patient reacts in the same normal fashion, don't worry. When you're in charge, he'll welcome you back with open arms. Continue to baby him, to make it all better. And know this for what it is because, my friend, this is a sort of weaning process. It is necessary for his security, and for your survival.

NOTES

Chapter Sixteen

DO THE BEST YOU CAN
WITH WHAT YOU'VE GOT

- Help him realize it isn't always necessary to give up one's work.
- Promote his interest in a fascinating hobby.
- Encourage him to go to his "office."
- Tell him you know he can do it.
- Give him an unexpected squeeze.

DO THE BEST YOU CAN WITH WHAT YOU'VE GOT

For the past year or so I have been writing and producing a documentary with a talented young director named Marshall Thompson. It deals with Jim's years as a Parkinson's patient. Specifically, it's about the fact that it isn't always necessary to give up one's career, or job, or hobby, despite illness. During the time Jim was sick, he acted in two movies — *Prince Jack*, about the Kennedys, and *Slapstick*, the 1984 film by Kurt Vonnegut in which Jimmy played the President of the United States. With me as his collaborator during his illness, as I mentioned earlier, Jim also wrote two books (*Backus Strikes Back* in 1984 and *Forgive Us Our Digressions* in 1988) and a play, *Celebrity A.A.* He also continued to do his La-Z-Boy commercials, and had been their spokesman for many years. In his spare time, the man who had said, "Don't buy me any more paints or sketch pads; I have no talent," spent many a moment engrossed in making charmingly funny drawings. Somehow all this was managed in between all of Jim's Parkinson's chores. Admittedly, the makers of the movies and commercials had very kindly altered their schedules to accommodate his illness. If Jim had been forced to give up acting altogether, I think that would have been the end.

Most people who have jobs or activities they love feel as Jim did. Our business manager, Charlie

Goldring, is one of them. Parkinson's disease has not kept him from his office. Granted, he doesn't come in every day, and he leaves a little early. But he's where he wants to be. And all of his clients are, as ever, perfectly taken care of. His office is still, as Jim's grandmother used to say, "a going Jessie."

Then there's Eric, my needlepoint man, an artist at what he does. This poor beknighted soul has been putting my rugs, pillows, and whatever else I have desecrated into some kind of shape for years. He has blocked them and mounted them and made them look like I know what I'm doing. His work is still as meticulous and beautiful as ever, and Eric has had this disease for over twenty years. But he's still there!

And there's Mary-Beth. She always adored beautiful gardens and lusted after one of her own, but never got around to doing anything about it. Too busy to find a house with a garden. So she is still in her apartment, which has a large balcony. Now, with Parkinson's disease, she has taken up pot gardening. Her balcony is a visual delight, a veritable showplace. She works every spare moment at her hobby and has recently gotten involved in raising orchids. I am especially thrilled by this turn of events, as I am the recipient of a breathtaking Phalaenopsis!

We once met a Parkinson's patient at physical therapy who used to consider it an affront to have to walk half a block to wherever he was parked. He is now a walking junkie with earphones soldered to his head.

Another patient, a woman who had never cooked, found herself alone one day and hungry. She made herself a sandwich. It was wonderful. Now that's all she wants to eat, and she talks hopefully of when she gets well and can open a sandwich and stew bar. Not a bad idea!

And this one simply amazed me. I recently met a man at a Parkinson's meeting who still plays tennis. A remarkable feat in any case, since he is in his eighties!

So you see, continuing to stay busy, active and involved is very important, even if participation has to be modified to accommodate physical limitations and changing capabilities. Work and hobbies are integral to life, and they need not stop — unless of course you're into bungee jumping or watch repair.

The point is, as Jim's analyst said, "Never give up!" You can do it. Just remember, "Do the best you can with what you've got!"

Chapter Seventeen

GO WITH IT

- Buy him a beautiful cane.
- Trim his eyebrows.
- Find his glasses.
- Find his other shoe.
- Find his keys.
- Put his handkerchief in a convenient pocket.
- Try to anticipate him.
- Smile.
- Tell him he's wonderful.

GO WITH IT

In early January of 1986, Jim was suddenly very strange. This time it was different. I thought it might be because our anniversary was coming up. A landmark. A date. It's later than you think. Or could it be his approaching birthday with its accompanying blues? This one was odd. He wasn't depressed. It wasn't a panic. He was just weird. He clung to me, wouldn't leave me alone for a minute. He just hung on and followed me around. I couldn't pull him out of it. It was exhausting, to say nothing of confusing. I was going a little crazy and finally exploded — hating myself, of course, through it all. I couldn't stop, but I did find out what was bothering him. He had faithfully promised George Burns, whom he loved, whom everybody loved, that he would absolutely, positively attend George's ninetieth birthday party — a date which was almost upon us. Jim was terrified. The party was tomorrow, and he was petrified and torn. I don't know what I said or did, but with great good luck I simmered both of us down, and we got through the night. I'm going to give you a page out of my diary, verbatim:

<u>January 11, 1986</u>

This was a toughie. Getting Jim to go to George's party. Just getting him up and moving! He was sick with indecision and terror all day. Thank God Freddie was due to do our hair and bathe and dress Jim. Then I could have a little private time to get myself glued together. Jim looked so handsome. Freddie did a great job on him. He was cheerful. Just fine. I guess looking good is the best revenge....

The party was a gas. We saw so many old friends. Sweet George made much of Jimmy, who basked in it. He must have felt that he was back where he belongs. He had such a wonderful time that when it was over he insisted we go to Matteo's for a nightcap. We went and, though it was barely midnight, it was closed.

Not to worry. I gave him a little something later when he was safely at home in bed. He thanked me, kissed me and cuddled, and went happily to sleep.

Though it wore me out to get him there, the next day he had no whammies, no depression — just happiness. He reminisced all that day about his last night's success — and swam four extra widths all on his own!

I don't say it always works this way, but it's really worth everything you can give it to get your patient to go out in style once in a while, especially if he's made a commitment. Better he face going out than suffer the regrets afterward, which are bound to be enormous.

I remember Jim telling me what his analyst said after he told him his George Burns experience. He said, "I'm proud of you, Jimmy! You got

moving. Keep moving! And always remember this
— do the best you can with what you've got. And
how about a little prayer? Try the AA prayer:

> God grant me the serenity to accept the
> things I cannot change,
> The courage to change the things I can,
> And the wisdom to know the difference."

Chapter Eighteen

PAIN

- Save cup-shaped tops of containers and measure into them a week's worth of his medications.
- Use your alarm clock or kitchen timer to signal the time to give them to him.
- Take him to a gentle dentist.
- Leave a little love note beside him when he's napping.

PAIN

When Dr. Parkinson came up with his charming malaise he didn't miss a trick. They really ought to rename it "Catch 22." Just when you have one element contained, another rears its catastrophic head.

Parkinson's disease does not cause the kind of pain that requires narcotic or analgesic drugs for relief. There are, though, various types of pain that may be experienced. Jim encountered some of them, including cold feet. His feet would feel warm to the touch, but to him they were frozen. A hot water bag was useful, and he always wore warm socks in bed. This will help. Or you might use your heating pad.

Another nuisance was dry eyes, which would sometimes glue his lids together. The remedy for that is "artificial tears." There are many varieties on the market; ask your doctor which one he recommends.

And then there were cramps. Foot cramps, which happened often, usually came on in the night. This can be very, very uncomfortable, and even alarming. Have him get out of bed as quickly as possible and stamp on that foot. Massage can also help. Just rub it until the pain subsides. Sometimes Jim would get a cramp in his leg. This always seemed to occur in the daytime. After you have massaged it and it seems to be lessening, have him walk in exaggerated parade fashion with the knees up high until the pain has completely disappeared.

If he's inclined toward leg cramps, when your patient takes his normal walks have him walk in modified parade style, knees higher than usual, and be sure he swings his arms. This will help his balance and the parade strut may reduce his leg cramps.

One of Jim's trips to the hospital was the result of low blood pressure, which was caused by his rising too quickly from his chair. It can also happen on first arising in the morning. Always insist that your patient rise slowly. If his blood pressure is sufficiently low, he may have symptoms of weakness, fatigue, dizziness, and light-headedness when rising from a seated position. In Jim's case, and this is often so, it was caused by his medications and was quickly and easily corrected.

When a Parkinson's patient cannot sleep, the problem is seldom at the beginning of bedtime. Many patients, like Jim, fall asleep rather easily and then awaken later. Sometimes it is a matter of when nature calls, but often it is simply a Parkinson's pattern. If sleep becomes a real problem, please discuss it with your doctor. Never, never give the patient one of your sleeping pills, or anybody else's. And under no condition ever give the patient an over-the-counter drug such as Sominex, or any other sleeping aid, as they may cause a dangerous interaction with anti-Parkinson's drug treatments. Once again, check with your doctor.

When Jim awoke in the night I would give him what he called a "Brandy milk punch," which never failed to work. I made it out of hot milk, a shot of brandy, and a sprinkle of nutmeg on the top.

His nice mug with the handle and the artistic sprinkle of nutmeg must have made it look like what Jim believed to be a real "brandy milk punch," whatever that is. Or, who knows? Maybe it was!

Chapter Nineteen

MYSTERY PAIN

- Keep a written record of all his symptoms.
- Never take too much upon yourself.
- Call your doctor.
- Follow his suggestions.
- Remind your patient that he's a darling.

MYSTERY PAIN

There is also a hideous business known as "mystery pain." Some very inexplicable things happened to Jim — like this one.

At one point Jim promised to make a taped spot for a charity. He was to do a short spiel and then sing a ditty as Mr. Magoo. He accepted — thinking, no doubt, that the taping day would never come — and promptly forgot all about it.

But that day did come, and with it a giant case of what Jim used to call "the whips and jangles." He was terrified, and, once again, torn. And once again he faced it and did what was expected of him. He went to the studio with his manager, Jack Lloyd, and somehow managed to get through it.

When it was over, the panic gone, he was elated to see me and eager to have me hear about the whole thing. Apparently, though, it had been such a frightening ordeal that he recalled very little of it. "You tell her, Jack," he said.

"Well," said Jack, "I told them Jim was too shaky to stand up, so they rigged up a chair with a music stand beside it for his script."

Jim looked at Jack like a grateful calf. "I don't remember how I did it," said Jim. "Technique over terror, I guess. I simply do not remember." Then he added, "I guess the chair and the music stand did the trick."

After a long pause, Jack said, "Jim, you never used that music stand, or that chair. Not once!"

"Never used the chair?" asked an amazed Jim.

"No. As Magoo you were jumping all over the place. And boy did you sing! Funny thing, though, when you did the intro as yourself, then you did sit in the chair. I mean, you were so weak we could hardly hear you. Your voice went. They had to jack up the sound."

Well, that's it! That's what actually happened. It's like the classic tale of the terrified ventriloquist and his nervy dummy. It's hard to explain, but it actually has happened in one form or another with many Parkinson's patients.

For many months Jim suffered the agonies of the damned from pain in his prostate. It had him climbing the walls. I couldn't bear to watch it, and there didn't seem to be anything that anyone could do. Each and every doctor told him it did not exist. That it was all imaginary. "Ignore it, Jimmy. It's all in your head." There was no way. It simply persisted and seemed to get worse. We tried everything; nothing helped — not exercise, rest, relaxation tapes, prayers, mystics, or the laying on of hands, which we also tried in desperation and in vain. We took a stab at anything anyone suggested. It was horrendous. There was nothing to be done about it.

Finally Jim insisted and insisted that it was cancer. He became so obsessed and so ill that the only answer was to operate, to go in there and check it out for him. The surgery was performed quickly by an esteemed surgeon, who checked it thoroughly and told Jim there was nothing there, he was clean as a whistle, and to forget about it.

Would you believe that from that moment on Jimmy never had a sign of pain? Not one. Not ever. Nothing. We still don't know what that was all about, but it does happen.

Please don't ever take it on yourself to think the pain your patient is complaining about is only a phantom. While it occasionally does occur, it is relatively rare and needs the most careful kind of checking. Call your doctor to get to the bottom of anything that may be even slightly mysterious.

Chapter Twenty

HELP FOR THE HELPMATE

- Have an overall system.
- Keep a diary.
- Have a pocket-size address book of his doctors, etc.
- Take a nap with him.
- Be there for yourself.
- Get your hair done.
- Go shopping.

HELP FOR THE HELPMATE

Yours is a vital role. As you know, it takes love and dedication. And since you are such an important cog in this wheel, you have to keep oiled up, which is just another way of saying you need stamina. Maybe some of the things I did for myself will work for you.

I've already mentioned a few that I did to keep going, but I don't think any of them would have been of any value without an overall system.

My big help was keeping a diary, or a journal, or a log, or whatever you want to call it. Whatever it was, everything was written down in it. I could see it, I could refer to it, and I could also refer back to it. I kept very careful records of how each day went. I made detailed notes on Jim's entire condition — appetite, voiding, bowels, sleep, rest, moods. It got to be so routine that I was able to do this with my own invented symbols, a sort of personal shorthand. Then on our visits to the doctor I had a detailed summary that he was able to absorb quickly. Our physician found this very helpful and suggested that I keep one on myself, too. Then anything that was out of line for either of us was there in black and white and could be caught early and corrected. This way we could not forget items that were seemingly unimportant but might later prove significant. Equally important, writing it down meant one less thing I was required to keep in my memory and on my mind.

To keep my health, my sanity, and my

patience (believe me, I would like to match the patience of a Parkinson's patient), I had to have a good night's sleep. As I mentioned earlier, mine was interrupted all through the night. I had had many years of sleep problems, and at one time had been helped by hypnosis, which still worked. So now I was able to fall back to slumberland easily, even on those nights when I fell asleep on the bathroom floor while Jim sat on the john with his hot water bottle, hoping for some action. Can you believe this is possible for an ex-insomniac? Well, that's what worked for me. There will be something to help you here, too. If you need to, you must certainly consult your doctor.

As I told you, to get periods of rest during those busy, stress-filled days, I would lie down whenever Jim took his nap and, as you know, I found some of his relaxation tapes as helpful as he did.

I don't have to dwell on exercise. You'll get plenty of that anyway, and a lot more by doing his physical therapy moves with him. And all that dancing. And don't forget that little extra dividend if you have stairs!

It is important that you be able to keep your own doctor and dentist appointments and that you stay attractive. In sum, you must be there for yourself as you are for your patient. It should be possible for you to manage your normal visits to the beauty parlor, the dry cleaners, the dressmaker. A little shopping wouldn't hurt either.

Try to keep your life in order. To be cheerful. To be your best you. Don't ever forget that you have a major role. What could be better than to hear him say, "My, you look lovely. How could I ever live without you!"

Chapter Twenty-one

CODA

- Hold him tight....

CODA

Those ten-and-a-half years I spent taking care of the man I love were terrible and, somehow, wonderful. I gave as much of myself as I had to give and, oh, how it was returned. We were always very close, but this brought us, if possible, even closer. What memories we make!

It was so very hard. Just remember to take care of your own health — physical, emotional, and psychological. Try to be patient, with yourself and with him. Try to understand and anticipate him. And, of course, give him all your love.

Someday soon they will find the way out. I had pie-in-the-sky dreams of a cure in time for Jim. May they find it soon.

In the meantime, stay well, and when things get tough, try to disconnect your emotional machinery for a while. Take good care of him; take good care of yourself. Love him; know that he loves you. Hold him; let him be empowered by holding you.

I will always hold Jimmy and, as I stand on the brink of tomorrow, I haven't forgotten the music.

Now, as we come down the homestretch, I hope that I have made you feel that you have a friend. In trying to help you, in recalling those years with Jim so accurately, you have helped me. I feel much less alone, and it has brought Jim into the present. He seems much closer. I am very thankful for that. Let's always remember that love is the strongest force in the world. We can give it away and give it away, and still have more than ever.

Thank you, and thanks for reading.

And, as my Irish friends always say…

Cheery-bye!

NOTES

EPILOGUE

There it was, the graceful dragonfly with the golden wings. No matter what time of day I chose to swim, there it would be — close above me as I sailed up and down the water doing my backstroke laps. Though we swim all year 'round in California, my swimming companion appeared only in the summertime, all through those seven sad years since Jimmy was called away forever. It simply flew above me, never once trying to sew up my mouth, even though they assured me at recess that these creatures, known to us in those days as "darning needles," surely would.

This year was no different. It was always there to greet me on my first lap, to simply fly away when I leaped from the water at the end.

I never caught sight of it at any other time. Not when I was picking flowers, or plucking lemons from the tree. Not even on those lovely barefoot days when I simply strolled around the garden on the soft, sweet grass.

This summer my dragonfly was there as usual, greeting me on my first lap and flying away at the end.

One day, before I dived in, I saw it lying by the side of the pool very quietly. It couldn't be! Not my lovely lively little dragonfly! I tentatively approached, and there it was in all its golden-winged beauty. So still. Dead? Surely it was dead. No more my little flitting friend flying above me to guide me and protect me and keep me company since Jimmy was no longer there swimming by my side.

I couldn't let the gardener take care of this glorious little body. I would go in and get the gift box and some soft tissue and bury it right here beside the pool.

Just as I was about to move, it stirred, lifted itself up, and flew to the end of the pool, waiting for me to dive in. I felt a great surge of relief as I quickly joined it. It was just taking a little nap, I laughed to myself.

From then on I found it napping in exactly the same spot every day, to awaken mysteriously just as I was about to begin. What had it been doing this summer that so tired it out? Where had it been? Where did it go every day? Where did it come from?

It is late September now. Yesterday was a most beautiful day, shimmering skies, air perfumed with the fall crop of orange blossoms. That's the way it always used to be, when the air was crystal clear and we could see for miles and all the buildings were low and white, and sometimes pink or blue. Yes, that's the way it used to be when the world and I were young.

My dragonfly wasn't there when I entered the water. I looked around. It was nowhere to be seen. With a heavy heart I started my swim. I plowed through my usual routine when, toward the end of my laps, I beheld him sitting, wings fully spread, right on his usual nap site. Beside him was another dragonfly, much larger with deep copper wings. They rose in tandem toward me, accompanying me throughout the last of my swim. They flew so close together, were they holding wings?

When I finished I leapt out and sat at the side of the pool for a moment. They flew toward me and circled me twice, still entwined, and then they flew off.

My heart sank. Was that farewell? No. Suddenly my spirits lifted, and I knew that if I waited and watched and kept on swimming, someday it would return, and my beautiful golden dragonfly would once again soar above me and we would go on flying across the water together forever.

CARE FOR THE CARETAKER

- Half fill his glass.
- Toast him with a pre-dinner drink.
- Double knot his shoelaces.
- Have handles installed on the stairway, shower, and beside the toilet and tub.
- Whisper, "I love you," in passing.
- Don't insist that he eat right now.
- In restaurants, order food that needs no cutting.
- Do the cologne and talcum powder ritual for him.
- Get in the tub with him.
- Take his arm as usual, but now let him lean on you.
- Leave a little love note beside him while he's napping.
- Keep it light.
- Keep a diary.
- Put his handkerchief in a convenient pocket.
- Keep a pocket-sized address book of his doctors, etc.
- Make friends with a druggist who delivers.
- Fluff his pillows.
- Change his light bulbs.
- Give him an emery board as a bookmark — it stays put.

- Give him a rubber band as a bookmark, if it's a paperback.
- Rent, borrow or buy him light and amusing books.
- Check your TV listing and avoid any hospital, medical, or other possibly upsetting shows.
- Hang on to your sense of humor.
- Hold him tight.
- Sneak a kiss on the back of his neck when he's reading.
- Keep him laughing.
- Rent light and funny movies.
- Before his nap time give him a beer in a mug with a handle.
- Sing in the car on the way to the doctor. Have him sing along with you.
- Do silly duets.
- Do his physical therapy exercises with him.
- Take walks with him.
- Have pretend Olympic races with him across a pool — *width*-wise.
- Have wrought iron banisters installed outside, especially at the pool.
- Introduce him to a bird and a butterfly.
- Tell him he's adorable.
- Have him do his tongue and vocal exercises into a little recorder.
- Sing to him even if you can't.

- Write him a poem, a limerick, another love note.
- If he has a tantrum and screams at you, make light of it and kiss his pointing finger.
- Be his best friend even on those days when he seems to have stopped being yours.
- Play his favorite music.
- Dance around the room and encourage him to join you.
- Ask him to show you how he used to "dance for Mommy."
- Tell him he's still the cutest.
- Be sure his window is partly opened if you have to leave him in the car alone.
- See that he's sitting down when he pulls on his pants.
- Never stop making loving gestures or telling him he's a darling.
- Put on his socks and shoes and slip him a little foot kiss.
- Make him wonderful nutritious drinks between meals.
- Give him one or two not-so-nutritious drinks before dinner.
- And give him a drink to sleep on — medication permitting, of course.
- Learn how to manicure his nails — give him a pedicure — maybe even cut his hair.
- Put a flower on his tray.

- Put a peppermint on his pillow.
- Fluff it up again.
- Learn to shave him.
- Take him for a drive off the beaten path and certainly off the freeway.
- If he enjoys it, next time try another pathway.
- Then allow time for that kind of offbeat drive wherever you go.
- Play board games with him that are easy to handle, like "Boggle."
- Play word games that need no props.
- Always enter the car singing after first seeing him safely seated.
- It may become habit for him too — then do your duets.
- Learn the lyrics to "his songs" — school, love, or pornographic.
- Keep him laughing.
- Buy him a harmonica — this aids tongue flexibility and breathing.
- Take him to a gentle dentist.
- Give him a massage with all the oils and unguents.
- Study the Kama Sutra.
- Use it!
- Give him a perfumed foot bath. Make rituals of these.
- Tell him he's your lord and master.

- Be a seducer.
- Give him a pillow roll and a triangular one for his back.
- Use one of them in the car, too.
- Buy him some soft, non-skid slippers.
- Protect him from drafts.
- Tuck a towel into the neck of his robe and tell him it makes him look sexy.
- Put a plastic fish and a rubber duck and a sailboat in his tub.
- Get large non-skid safety mats for the tub and the shower — always see that they are functioning.
- Buy him a relaxation tape, perhaps the sound of ocean waves or rain.
- Have cup-shaped tops of containers and measure into them a week's worth of his medications.
- Use your alarm clock or alarm watch to signal the time to give them to him.
- Don't be afraid to do the enemas yourself.
- Croon to him if he's frightened or embarrassed.
- Be patient.
- Learn to wait.
- Clean his eyeglasses.
- Take his pen away when he's finished to keep ink stains to a minimum.
- Keep him busy.

- Keep him laughing.
- Buy childproof stuff.
- Make lists and try to stick with them.
- Write things down — it helps.
- Use Post-It notes for reminders.
- Hold his hand to guide him when he brushes his teeth. If necessary, you do it and clean his bridges, too.
- Use short sentences.
- Enunciate.
- Find his keys.
- Find his glasses.
- Find his other shoe.
- Try to make a game of everything.
- Buy him a beautiful cane.
- Look at his yearbook with him.
- Look at his photo albums with him.
- Help him put them in order.
- Listen to his stories about those books again.
- Wipe his nose.
- And wipe him there, if he's unable to, but gently.
- Wrap him in the biggest bath sheet.
- Be absolutely sure to always have all wires and cords securely pinned back and out of the way.
- Plug in a good reading light.
- Walk up the stairs behind him.

- Walk down the stairs in front of him — backwards if you can.
- Try to let him do some things alone.
- Stand by — but subtly.
- Smile.
- Try a little baby talk.
- Tell him he's wonderful.
- Give him an unexpected squeeze.
- Massage his neck.
- Massage his back.
- Massage all of him.
- Scoop his soft-boiled eggs out of the shells.
- Get on the phone extension and translate if need be.
- Don't overwhelm him.
- Sleep so close you share one pillow.
- Don't hover.
- Trim his eyebrows.
- Hang on to your sense of humor.
- Try to anticipate him.
- Hug him.
- Keep calm.
- Keep him laughing
           and
       Hold him tight.

Henny's favorite picture of Jim

Jim's favorite picture of Henny